The Long Walk

The True Story of Molly Craig

Amy Zavatto

SCHOLASTIC INC.
New York Toronto London Auckland Sydney
Mexico City New Delhi Hong Kong Buenos Aires

Illustrations
Jeff Spokes

Text copyright © 2004 by Scholastic Inc.
Illustrations copyright © 2004 by Jeff Spokes.
All rights reserved. Published by Scholastic Inc.
Printed in the U.S.A.

ISBN 0-439-68246-0

1 2 3 4 5 6 7 8 9 10   23   12 11 10 09 08 07 06 05 04

Contents

Introduction

Aborigines were the first group of people to settle in Australia.

Many, many years later, white people from Europe moved there. These new **settlers** took over. Over time, they formed a government. Often, this government was not fair to Aborigines.

In 1931, the government looked for kids who had white fathers and Aboriginal mothers. They didn't want these kids to grow up with Aborigines. So they sent them to camps. There, the kids would learn

Aborigines the first people of Australia
settlers people who move to an area where not many people live

Australia: The Land Down Under

Joe LeMonnier © Scholastic Inc.

Australia is almost the size of the United States. But there are almost 15 times as many people in the U.S. as in Australia.

to live with and work for white people.

One of these kids was a girl named Molly Craig. She was taken away with her cousins Daisy and Gracie. A writer named Amy Zavatto **imagined** what this was like for Molly. Then Amy wrote this book.

imagined thought about what something might have been like

The day was like any other.
Then a strange man showed up.

1

A Happy Home

I was outside with Daisy and Gracie. They are my cousins. But we were like sisters. They often stayed with Momma and me.

We were playing tag. Daisy was chasing me. We used the rabbit-proof fence as the base. It was a long fence that was supposed to keep rabbits off our farm.

"You're it, Molly!" Daisy said.

I was playing tag with my two little cousins. The fence was base.

I let Daisy tag me because she's little. She's only eight. She can't run very fast. I'm 13. I'm much taller and stronger.

I ran after Gracie. She's ten and growing fast. "You're it!" I laughed when I finally caught her.

"Look, Molly. It's a car," Gracie said. She was breathing hard.

A big, black car was coming our way. A white man was driving it. Momma ran out of our house.

"Molly! Gracie! Daisy! Run and hide!" she yelled.

Not many cars came to our town of Jigalong. We lived in the desert. And when we did see a car, Momma always made us hide.

"Come on!" I yelled to Daisy and

Gracie. I grabbed their hands. We ran to the back of the house and hid.

"I want a drink of water!" said Daisy.

"Shhhh!" I said.

I could hear Momma yelling at the man. "There are no children here! Go away!" she said.

I heard the man's footsteps. He was coming toward us. He looked in our **outhouse**.

Then he saw us behind the house.

Why do you think Molly's mom is lying to the man?

outhouse an outside bathroom

The stranger takes the girls.
He says he's just obeying the law.

2

Taken Away

The man was big and scary looking. He was wearing a uniform. He looked mean. I picked up Daisy and Gracie and ran. But the man was too fast. He grabbed us and carried us to his car.

"No!" Momma screamed. "Don't take my girls!"

She tried to pull us away from him. But he was too big and strong.

"These girls are coming with me," he said. "It's the law."

"Why?" I yelled.

"Your mothers are Aboriginal. But your fathers are white, like me," the man said. "So you have to live with white people."

"What does Aboriginal mean?" I asked.

"It means your skin is dark, like your mother's," the man said. "Now stop asking questions. Get in!"

Momma tried again to grab us. The man pushed us into the car. Then he got in and drove off.

"Where are we going?" I asked him.

"Moore River Camp," he answered.

"Where is that?" I asked.

"It's in the south," he said.

I put my arms around Daisy and Gracie.

We watch Mama and the house disappear in a cloud of dust.

"It's okay," I told the girls. "We'll get back home. I promise."

We watched my house disappear in a cloud of dust. After awhile, the only **familiar** thing I saw was the rabbit-proof fence. It stretched on for miles and miles.

familiar well-known

Too Many Rabbits
Why was the rabbit-proof fence built?

In the 1800s, white Australians wanted to hunt. So they brought rabbits to eastern Australia.

It was a bad idea. Soon, there were too many rabbits. Rabbits started to **invade** farms in the west. They ate crops. They ate grass. They ate everything!

In 1907, the government decided to build a fence. Hopefully, it would keep the rabbits in the east.

The fence stretched from the top of Australia to the bottom. It covered about 1,000 miles. (See p. 17.)

Courtesy of Western Australia Tourism Council

But it was too late. There were already lots of rabbits in the west. After some time, the government decided to kill the rabbits.

The rabbit-proof fence was made of wooden posts and barbed wire. Many parts of it are still standing today.

invade to move into and take over

The girls are taken to a camp in the south.
They're a thousand miles from home.

3

The Camp

We drove north to the ocean and got on a boat. Then we sailed south for days. Gracie, Daisy, and I weren't used to the water. At first we were scared.

A white woman was waiting for the boat. "Come with me," she told us.

We got in her car. We drove for hours. We were very far south. Nothing looked familiar.

Then I thought about the rabbit-proof fence. That fence is really, really long. I knew that it had to be around there somewhere.

How did I know that? My father's job was to check the fence for holes. And he often traveled south to check it.

"Where's the rabbit-proof fence?" I asked the woman. "Isn't it near here?"

"It's not far," she said. "It's just east of Moore River Camp."

Soon, we got to Moore River Camp. Another white woman met us there.

"Welcome to your new home," she said.

"My home is in Jigalong!" cried Daisy.

The woman took us to a big building. There were lots of beds inside. There were also lots of children. They were dark like us.

"In you go," the woman said. I looked at the plain walls and bare floor. I thought about the roof of my home. It was made of hay and mud. It made the house smell sweet. This place didn't smell good at all.

A bell rang. All the children lined up by the door. It was time for lunch.

"Follow me!" I told Daisy and Gracie. We got in the back of the line. When the kids went outside, I grabbed my cousins and ran.

"Where are we going?" Daisy asked.

"We're going to find the rabbit-proof fence and follow it north to Jigalong!"

What is Molly's plan? Do you think it will work?

Following the Rabbit-Proof Fence
The girls planned to follow the fence north.

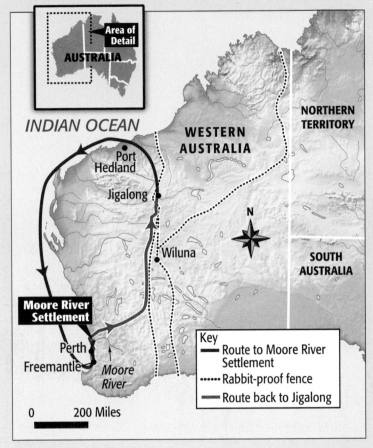

Area of Detail

AUSTRALIA

INDIAN OCEAN

NORTHERN TERRITORY

WESTERN AUSTRALIA

Port Hedland

Jigalong

N

Wiluna

SOUTH AUSTRALIA

Moore River Settlement

Perth

Freemantle

Moore River

Key
— Route to Moore River Settlement
····· Rabbit-proof fence
— Route back to Jigalong

0   200 Miles

Joe LeMo nier © Scholastic Inc.

Molly and the girls had been taken south to a camp near the Moore River. They were planning to walk 1,000 miles north to Jigalong.

Escaping was easy.
But getting home was going to be hard.

4

The Fence

I had a plan for finding the rabbit-proof fence. The woman had told me it was to the east. So we'd just walk in that direction. My grandmother had taught me how to use the sun as a guide. So I knew how to stay on course.

"Come on," I said to Daisy and Gracie. I pointed east. "We need to walk that way. Then we'll find the fence."

"And then we'll go home to Jigalong?" cried Daisy.

"That's right," I said. "We'll follow the fence home. I can't wait to see Momma."

"I wish I could see my momma, too," said Gracie.

Gracie's momma worked in a town called Wiluna. That's south of Jigalong. Gracie missed her mother very much.

We walked for days and days. At night, we'd dig a hole next to a tree. We slept in the hole to keep warm. In the mornings, we'd eat the fruit from the tree. I'd put some in my pockets for us to eat later.

Finally, we found the fence.

"There!" Gracie pointed. "I see it!"

We were tired. But seeing the fence gave us energy.

We followed the fence north. Sometimes I had to carry Daisy.

We turned to the north. We started walking along the fence.

The walk was very hot and tiring. Sometimes I had to carry Daisy.

We knew we had to be careful. We didn't want anyone to find us and send us back to the camp.

Gracie takes a big chance.
Will she get caught?

5

Gracie's Choice

We walked for three weeks. Then we came to a train station.

"This is the Mt. Russel Station," I said. "It's not far from home!"

Gracie looked sad. "I know this station," she said. "My momma takes the train from here to Wiluna."

I knew what Gracie was thinking. She wanted to take the train to Wiluna. There, she could look for her mother.

"Gracie, please don't do it," I said. "They'll catch you. And they'll take you back to that camp."

"I *won't* get caught," said Gracie. "And I want my momma!" She turned and ran toward the station.

"No, Gracie!" I yelled.

I saw a policeman walk by the station. I grabbed Daisy's hand. I pulled her behind some boxes. I held her in my arms.

We both were crying. I didn't know if Gracie would be caught. But I knew Daisy and I had to keep going.

"We have to go on, Daisy," I told her. "We can't give up."

Following in Their Footsteps
Everyone was looking for three little girls.

People were really upset when Molly, Gracie, and Daisy left the Moore River Camp. The government wanted to find the girls and send them back.

People figured out that the girls were trying to walk home. So, the government sent the police after the girls. They also hired special **trackers**. The trackers were told to look for tracks the girls made as they walked north.

The government also put an ad in a newspaper. Here's what the ad told readers.

Missing: Three Little Girls
Last Seen: August 14, 1931

The government is worried about three girls. A week ago, they ran away from the Moore River Camp. They are trying to get back home. Some people saw them a few days ago. The girls were walking north. The girls probably don't want people to see them. So they may be staying away from towns. Please look out for these girls. And tell the government if you see them.

trackers people who can follow tracks and other signs to find animals and people

The girls have walked for a month.
But now their trip has come to an end.

6

Back Home

Daisy and I kept walking. The land around us started to look familiar. I remembered that my Auntie lived near Jigalong. Then I saw her house.

Auntie was working outside.

"Girls!" she cried. She rushed over to us. She hugged us really hard.

"Everyone has been so worried about you!" she said. "But where's Gracie?"

"Gracie wanted to find her mother," I told my Auntie. "She ran off to the train station. We didn't go with her. We were afraid we'd get caught."

Auntie nodded her head. "You did the right thing, Molly."

We ate a huge meal of meat and bread and tea. We took a hot bath. Then we went to sleep in real beds.

The next day our cousin Joey was going to Jigalong. "I'll make sure you get home safely," he said.

We still had a few days' **journey** ahead of us. Joey made fires at night. He also told us stories.

One hot and sunny afternoon, we finally saw our home again.

"Look!" cried Daisy

---

journey a trip

I picked her up and swung her in the air. "I'll give you a piggyback ride, Daisy," I said. "Come on!"

My cousin hopped on my back. I could feel how thin she had become. I ran as fast as I could.

"Momma! Momma!" I cried. Momma ran outside.

"Where's Gracie?" she asked. I quickly explained.

Then she said, "Oh, my girls!" She started to cry with joy. Then she threw her arms around us. She gave us a million kisses and hugs.

Momma said, "They told me you girls ran away. I prayed that you would make it back."

Daisy said, "Molly found our way

Momma threw her arms around us and gave us a million hugs.

home." I could tell she was **proud** of me.

I told Momma what we had done. "We followed the rabbit-proof fence all the way home," I explained.

"You are brave, brave girls," she said.

We went into our house and told Momma the rest of our story. That night, we slept in our own beds again. We had been running for over a month.

"Good-night Molly," Daisy whispered to me in the dark.

"Good-night Daisy," I whispered back.

Do you think Molly and Daisy will be safe in Jigalong?

proud happy about something good someone has done

Molly's Story
What happened to Molly Craig?

Molly made it home from the Moore River camp. She hoped she'd never see it again. But she did.

Years went by. Molly got married. She had two girls. Their names were Doris and Annabelle.

One day, a man came to see Molly and her girls. He sent them to the Moore River camp!

At the camp, Molly took her baby, Annabelle, and walked home. She left Doris behind.

In 1971, the government stopped taking kids from their mothers. Molly and Doris finally saw each other again. Molly told Doris about her first journey to Jigalong. Doris thought it was a great story. So she wrote a book about it. It's called *Follow the Rabbit-Proof Fence*.

© Wide World Photos

Doris Pilkington, Molly Craig's daughter, wrote about Molly.

Glossary

Aborigines *(noun)* the first people of Australia

familiar *(adjective)* well-known

imagined *(verb)* thought about what something might have been like

invade *(verb)* to move into and take over

journey *(noun)* a trip

outhouse *(noun)* an outside bathroom

proud *(adjective)* happy about something good someone has done

settlers *(noun)* people who move to an area where not many people live

trackers *(noun)* people who can follow tracks and other signs to find animals and people